Patr
Gui
1999 Total Eclipse

Patrick Moore's Guide to the 1999 Total Eclipse

*All royalties from the sale of this book
go to The South Downs Planetarium Trust.*

B⊞XTREE

First published as *The West Country Eclipse: 11 August 1999* by
The South Downs Planetarium Trust in September 1998.

This revised edition published 1999 by Boxtree
an imprint of Macmillan Publishers Ltd
25 Eccleston Place London SW1W 9NF
Basingstoke and Oxford

www.macmillan.co.uk

Associated companies throughout the world

ISBN 0 7522 1814 X

Printed by Mackays of Chatham plc

Contents

Acknowledgements

The author of this book and the Trustees of The South Downs Planetarium Trust acknowledge with thanks the following individuals and organisations who have kindly assisted with the publication of this book: the late Paul Doherty for permission to reproduce Picture 1a; Lick Observatory for permission to reproduce Picture 1b; Dr John Mason for the photographs included as Pictures 4, 6a and 6b; Dr Nigel Evans for permission to reproduce his excellent photographs included as Pictures 3, 7, 8, 9 10, 11a and b; Drs Fred Espanek and Jay Anderson for permission to reproduce Figures 9, 12, 13, 14, 15, 16, 17 and 18 from *NASA Reference Publication 1398*; Michael Maunder and Springer-Verlag for permission to reproduce the information in Table 7, Chapter 9; Dan Newman for redrawing Figures 3, 4, 5, 6, 7, 8, 10 and 11.

Preface

At the moment, plans are being made to set up a major planetarium and science centre at Chichester in West Sussex. This ambitious project is being managed by The South Downs Planetarium Trust, which is a registered educational charity. There can be no doubt that a planetarium is the best way of introducing people to astronomy – which is, after all, the oldest and most fascinating of all the sciences.

Once it is completed, the planetarium and science centre will be of enormous educational benefit and will make a major contribution to the public understanding of science in general. In particular, I feel sure that young people will be encouraged to take up science as a career and perhaps become research scientists. We need these researchers; and where better to encourage them than in a planetarium.

A considerable sum of money has already been raised by the Trust – over £150,000 to date – but we are anxious to open the planetarium as soon as possible, because we know the good it will do. So more money is needed. That is why I am donating all royalties from sales of this book to The South Downs Planetarium Trust; I personally make no money out of it – and neither do I want to. I have been involved with the planetarium project from the outset, and I very much hope that we shall be able to open our skies to the public in the not too distant future. With your help we can do so.

Patrick Moore
Selsey, April 1998

Chapter 1

11 AUGUST 1999

Have you ever seen a total eclipse of the Sun, arguably the grandest sight in all Nature? Possibly not. If you have spent your entire life in mainland Britain, your last chance was on 29 June 1927, and then only if you lived in North Wales and northern England. The total eclipse of 30 June 1954 did pass across the northernmost of the Shetland Islands, but it missed the mainland altogether. Now a new opportunity lies close ahead. Go to the south-west of England – the Scilly Isles and parts of Cornwall and Devon – on 11 August 1999 and, clouds permitting, you will be able to see the full glory of totality.

It will not last for long. Even at the most favourable sites – Penzance, Helston and Falmouth in Cornwall, for example – the total phase will be seen for only just over two minutes. From Newton Abbot in Devon it will be a mere 30 seconds. Stray as far as Launceston or Exeter and you will miss totality altogether, so you will have to choose your observing site very carefully. Moreover, there is always a considerable danger that the sky will be overcast at the critical moment, and, short of going up in an aircraft, which is far from ideal, there is nothing to be done about this. We must be honest; if you want to have

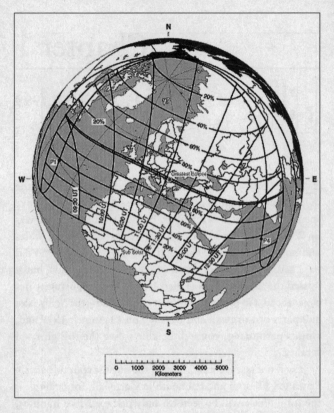

Figure 1: The path of totality across the Earth's surface on 11 August 1999.

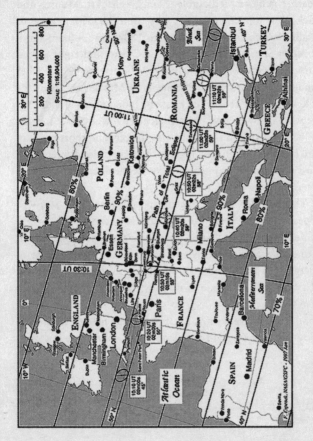

Figure 2: The path of totality across Europe on 11 August 1999.

a better chance of seeing totality against a clear sky, then you may be advised to travel to, say, parts of Europe where the weather is more predictable. Reims, Stuttgart, Munich and Bucharest, for example, are all within the critical zone of totality, which extends from about 180 miles (300km) south of Nova Scotia over the Atlantic Ocean and right across Europe as shown in Figures 1 and 2. Indeed the best weather conditions will probably be found in the Middle East which the path of totality crosses *en route* to India where it ends. Yet there are many people – myself included – who prefer to trust to luck and stay in the south-west of England. Fortune may well be kind; we can only hope so, because if clouds prevail we must wait until 23 September 2090 for the next total eclipse to be visible from mainland Britain.

This booklet, then, concentrates on the eclipse as it will appear from the West Country, and is intended to be a general guide. Note, please, that because British Summer Time (which is one hour ahead of Greenwich Mean Time) will then be in operation, I have used it throughout – so that, for example, 11h 12m BST (the time of mid-totality in Falmouth) is 10h 12m GMT.

So let us make a start. But first, it may help to say a little about the make-up of the Solar System – our home in space.

Chapter 2

EARTH, SUN AND MOON

Most people nowadays know that the Earth is a planet, moving round the Sun, but not everyone realises that the Sun, which looks so glorious to us, is nothing more than an ordinary star; indeed, astronomers go as far as to relegate it to the status of a stellar dwarf. The stars visible on any clear night are themselves suns, many of them far larger, hotter and more luminous than ours, but of course they are a great deal further away. The distance between the Earth and the Sun is, in round figures, 93 million miles (or, if you prefer metric, 150 million kilometres); the nearest star is over 25 million million miles (40 million million km) away. Represent the Earth-Sun distance by one inch (2.5 cm), and the nearest star will have to be taken out to 4.3 miles (6.9 km).

Then there is the question of size. The Earth's diameter is 7,926 miles (12,756 km), while that of the Sun is almost 865,000 miles (1,392,000 km), so you could pack a million Earths inside the huge solar globe and still leave room to spare. Yet the Sun is 'only' 330,000 times as massive as the Earth, because it is made up of gas rather than being solid and rocky. It is also very hot, with a surface temperature of 5,500 degrees Celsius, while near its core the temperature rises to the staggering value of around 15 million degrees. This means that to the casual observer the Sun is dangerous. Staring at it is decidedly unwise, and to look straight at it through a telescope or pair of binoculars will mean permanent blindness; even conventional dark filters are inadequate protectors. I will come back to this theme again and again throughout the booklet, and I make no apology for so doing, because there have been many tragic accidents in the past.

Round the Sun move the planets, the main members of the Solar System. The system is divided into two well-marked parts. First there are four relatively small, solid planets: Mercury, Venus, the Earth and Mars. Then comes a wide gap, occupied by a swarm of miniature rocky worlds known as the minor planets or asteroids, beyond which we come to the four giant planets: Jupiter, Saturn, Uranus and Neptune, plus one small maverick, Pluto, which does not seem to fit into the general pattern, and may not be worthy of true planetary status. To the naked eye, the planets look like stars, but they have no light of their own and shine only by reflected sunlight. Because some of them may well be seen during totality in 1999, I have summarised their main data in Table 1.

Of the nine planets listed in Table 1, the last three were not known in ancient times simply because they are too faint and remote, so they need concern us no further for the moment. Mercury always remains inconveniently close to the Sun in the sky, so that with the naked eye a total solar eclipse provides a good opportunity for seeing it. Venus, Jupiter and sometimes Mars may far outshine any star, and Saturn is also bright enough to be conspicuous.

The stars are so far away that their individual or 'proper' motions are very slight, and the star-patterns or constellations do not change appreciably over periods of many lifetimes; the constellations we see today – Orion, the Great Bear and the rest – are to all intents and purposes the same as they were

Table 1: The Planets

Planet	Mean distance from the Sun		Orbital period ('year')	Equatorial diameter		Rotation period
	millions of miles	millions of km		miles	km	
Mercury	36.0	57.9	88.0d	3,031	4,878	58.6d
Venus	67.2	108.2	224.7d	7,521	12,104	243.0d
Earth	93.0	149.6	365.2d	7,926	12,756	23h 56m
Mars	141.6	227.9	687.0d	4,222	6,794	24h 37m
Jupiter	483.6	778.3	11.9y	88,848	142,984	9h 50m
Saturn	886.7	1426.9	29.5y	74,902	120,540	10h 14m
Uranus	1,783.0	2869.4	84.0y	31,764	51,118	17h 14m
Neptune	2,794.0	4496.4	164.8y	30,776	49,528	16h 7m
Pluto	3,666.3	5900.2	247.7y	1,442	2,320	6.39d

in the time of King Canute, Julius Caesar or even the builders of the Pyramids. The planets on the other hand, wander slowly around, but they keep to a definite belt round the sky, known as the Zodiac, because (apart from Pluto) their paths or orbits lie in much the same plane. Draw a plan of the Solar System on a flat piece of paper, and you are not very far wrong. During the totality in 1999, the Sun will lie in the obscure Zodiacal constellation of Cancer, the Crab.*

Some of the planets have secondary bodies, or satellites, moving round them. Saturn has at least eighteen. Earth, however, has only one: our familar Moon, which is our closest neighbour in space, and stays together with us in our never-ending journey round the Sun. Its mean distance from Earth (centre to centre) is only 238,860 miles (384,400 km), and its revolution period is about 27.3 days. It is much smaller than the Earth, with a diameter of only 2,160 miles (3,476 km), and it is also much less massive; put the Earth in one pan of a gigantic pair of scales, and you would need 81 Moons to balance it. Its gravitational pull is much weaker than ours, and it has been unable to hold on to any atmosphere it may once have had, so that it is now airless, waterless and lifeless. Its surface is covered with mountains, craters, and broad darkish plains which are still mis-called 'seas' even though they are bone-dry. Even binoculars will show a wealth of details upon its disk, and there is no danger here, because the Moon sends us very little heat. You may dazzle yourself, but you cannot hurt your eyes.

Obviously the Sun can light only one half of the Moon at

---

* In fact a 'constellation' means nothing at all, because the stars are at very different distances from us, and we are dealing with nothing more significant than line-of-sight effects. Astrologers, who claim to link the positions of the planets with human character and destiny, pay great attention to the Zodiacal constellations, but it is fair to say that astrology proves only one scientific fact: 'There's one born every minute!'

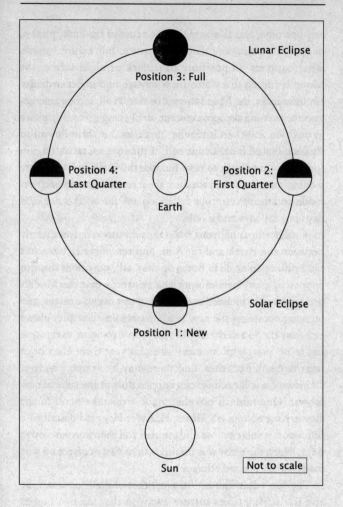

Figure 3: The phases of the Moon.

any one time, and this explains the cause of the lunar phases, or apparent changes of shape from new to full. Figure 3 shows what happens. In position 1 the dark or night side of the Moon is turned toward us (new moon), and under ordinary circumstances, the Moon cannot be seen at all. It then emerges into the evening sky as a crescent, thickening up to half phase at position 2. When it reaches position 3 it shows us all of its illuminated half, and is full; it then wanes to half again (position 4) and back to new. Because the Earth and Moon are moving together round the Sun, the interval between one new moon and the next (or one full moon and the next) is not 27.3 days but 29 days and a half.

A solar eclipse happens when the new moon passes directly between the Earth and the Sun, and temporarily blots out the brilliant solar disk. But, you may ask, why does this not happen at every new moon? The answer is that the Moon's orbit is tilted or inclined at an angle of just over 5 degrees, and on most occasions the new moon passes unseen either above or below the Sun in the sky. For an eclipse to occur, everything has to be 'just right'. In every calendar year there must be at least two solar eclipses, and there may be as many as five. Obviously, a solar eclipse can happen only at the time of new moon. (One famous novelist made a mistake here. In the classic *King Solomon's Mines*, H. Rider Haggard described a full moon, a solar eclipse and another full moon on successive days. When the error was pointed out, a hasty correction was made for the second edition!)

The Sun's diameter is 400 times that of the Moon, but the Sun is also 400 times further away, so that the two bodies appear virtually the same size in the sky (see Pictures 1a and b), and during a total eclipse the Moon is just large enough to cover the Sun completely. Many people have wondered why this is so. The answer is – sheer luck! If the Moon were slightly smaller, or slightly further away, it could never produce a total eclipse, so that in this respect we are decidedly fortunate. Because of the tidal effects, which need not concern us here, the Moon is slowly receding from the Earth; the rate of recession is currently less than 4 centimetres per year, but over the ages it mounts up, and the last total solar eclipse will happen in around one thousand million years from now. Whether there will be any astronomers left on Earth to observe it remains to be seen.

Before leaving the diagram given here, consider the situation when the Moon is full (position 3). Like all non-luminous bodies, the Earth casts a shadow in space, and if the Moon passes into this cone of shadow its supply of direct sunlight is cut off, producing a lunar eclipse. The Moon turns a dim, often coppery-red colour, before passing out of the shadow again. In general it does not vanish completely, because some of the Sun's rays are bent or refracted onto the Moon by way of the layer of atmosphere surrounding the Earth, but there are times when the eclipsed Moon is hard to trace with the naked eye; everything depends upon conditions in the Earth's upper air through which the refracted sunlight has to pass. Lunar eclipses may be either total or partial, and as seen from any particular location on Earth are more common than eclipses of the Sun because a lunar eclipse can be seen from any location from which the Moon is above the horizon at the time; this is not true of solar eclipses, as we will see in Chapter 4. The next total lunar eclipse visible from Britain is due on 21 January 2000, in the early hours of the morning. Watch out for it.

Chapter 3

DAYTIME STAR

The Sun is the only star which is sufficiently close to us to be examined in detail, and solar observation is a favourite pastime among amateur astronomers, but there are various rules which must always be borne in mind. Remember, the Sun is dangerous. This is true even when the Sun is low down over the horizon, and looks deceptively dim and harmless. You have only one pair of eyes, and a single careless mistake can have tragic consequences.

If you have a telescope, there are ways of observing the Sun without any risk which will enable you to see the yellowish disk, often with the dark patches known as sunspots. But under NO circumstances should you point the telescope at the Sun and then look straight through it, even when a dark filter has been fixed over the eyepiece. No ordinary filter can give proper protection. Moreover, a dark filter at the eyepiece end of the telescope (where the Sun's heat is concentrated) is always liable to shatter without the slightest warning. This was brought home to me many years ago, at a meeting of the British Astronomical Association – it must have been during the 1930s. I was talking to a man in his seventies, who was blind in one eye. He told that this went back to his boyhood, when he was using a 3-inch refracting telescope for direct solar observation. Of course a dark filter had been attached, but the filter suddenly cracked, and he was unable to shift his eye out of the way in time. There is only one rule for looking straight at the Sun through a telescope: DON'T. Unfortunately, some small telescopes are still sold together with dark 'sun-caps', which, the makers claim, are safe. Believe me, they are not.

Telescopes are of two main types: refractors and reflectors. A refractor collects its light by means of a lens known as an object-glass; the light passes down a tube and the rays are brought to focus, forming an image which is enlarged by a second lens termed an eyepiece. A reflector of the usual Newtonian pattern collects its light by means of a curved mirror; the rays are sent back up the tube to a smaller flat mirror inclined at an angle of 45 degrees, and this flat mirror sends the rays out to the side of the tube, where an image is formed and is magnified by an eyepiece as before. Either type can be used for solar work, but a refractor is much to be preferred.

The best and most sensible way to look at sunspots is to aim the telescope at the Sun, without looking through it, and then project the image onto a white card held or fixed behind the eyepiece, as shown in Picture 2 and Figure 4. Good views will be obtained in this way, and it is fascinating to follow the sunspot groups as they shift and change from day to day – even hour to hour. A refractor with an object-glass two or three inches (5 to 7.5 cm) in diameter is ideal; with a larger lens it is usually wise to 'stop down', because there is plenty of lighty to spare. True, there are various special devices which are harmless enough if properly used, and for safe observation of the partial phases of a solar eclipse many observers use filters made of what is termed mylar; I will have

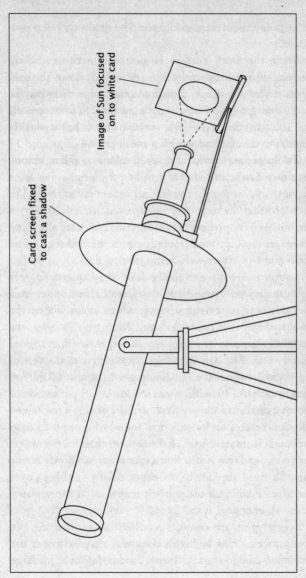

Image of Sun focused on to white card

Card screen fixed to cast a shadow

Figure 4: Projecting the Sun using a small telescope.

more to say about these in Chapter 5 – but always be on your guard.

Since the Sun's surface is gaseous, there can be no permanent features, and there are periods when the disk appears virtually blank, though at other times there may be many spot-groups on view at the same time. In some respects the Sun must be classed as a variable star. It has a roughly regular cycle of activity with a mean period of around 11 years. Spots are plentiful at times of solar maximum; activity then dies down, and after a protracted minimum the spots begin to appear again. The last maximum fell at the end of 1990, so that the next may be expected around 2001; it is impossible to be precise, because no two cycles are alike, and moreover some are much more energetic than others. During 1996 and 1997 there were many spotless days.

Sunspots are not genuinely dark; they appear so only because they are around 1,000 degrees Celsius cooler than the surrounding bright surface, which is known as the photosphere. If it could be seen shining on its own, the surface brightness of a spot would be greater than that of an arc-lamp. The largest spot-group ever recorded – that of April 1947 – reached a maximum size of almost 50 million square miles (130 million square km), and persisted for months; smaller spots may have lifetimes of only a few hours. The Sun rotates on its axis in a period of around 25 days (although it rotates faster at the equator than it does nearer the poles), and this means that a spot is carried slowly across the disk from one side to the other, finally vanishing over the edge or limb; subsequently it reappears at the opposite limb – if, of course, it still exists.

Single spots are common enough but most appear in groups, which may be highly complex; a typical group has two main components, a 'leader' and a 'follower'. A large spot has a darker central portion or umbra, surrounded by a lighter penumbra; there may be many umbrae contained within one mass of penumbra, and the details may be so complicated that they are difficult to draw; serious solar observers will always prefer photography. By the time of the 1999 eclipse, the Sun will be working up toward its next maximum, and there ought to be plenty of spot-groups, though one can never be sure.

It cannot be said that we have a full understanding of sun-spots, but they are certainly associated with magnetic phenomena, and may be regarded as regions where the lines of the solar magnetic field break through the surface. Associated with them are bright regions known as faculae (Latin, 'torches'), which are luminous clouds lying above the general level of the photosphere. Even in non-spot regions, the Sun's surface is never calm; it has a granular structure, and the general situation has been compared with that of a boiling liquid, though the photosphere is of course entirely gaseous.

Most of our knowledge of the Sun comes not from sheer visual observation, but from instruments based upon the principle of the spectroscope. The first steps were taken as long ago as 1666, by Isaac Newton, but the true science of solar spectroscopy dates back only to the early years of the nineteenth century, with the work of the German optician Josef von Fraunhofer.

Light is a wave-motion, and the colour of the light depends upon its wavelength – that is to say, the distance between one wave-crest and the next. Red light has the longest wavelength of visible light and violet the shortest, with orange, yellow, green, blue and indigo in between. (Of course, all these wavelengths are very short indeed by everyday standards; they are usually measured in units known as nanometres – one nanometre – nm – is equal to a ten-millionth part of a centimetre. The diameter of a human hair is roughly 150,000 nm). In 1814 Fraunhofer passed a beam of sunlight through a slit, and found that the light was spread out into a rainbow band, with red at one end and violet at the other. Fraunhofer also found that the band was crossed with dark lines, which always remained in the same positions and with the same intensities; these are still often called Fraunhofer lines, though they are more properly termed absorption lines. They were interpreted in 1859 by two other Germans, G. Kirchhoff and R. Bunsen, whose work really marked the beginning of what we may term modern-type studies of the Sun.

An incandescent solid, liquid, or gas at high pressure yields a rainbow or continuous spectrum, but an incandescent gas at lower pressure will produce a spectrum made up of disconnected lines, each of which is characteristic of one particular element or group of elements. For instance, incandescent sodium – one of the two main elements making up common salt – will produce, among others, two prominent yellow lines; if these are seen, they must be due to sodium and nothing else. The solar photosphere produces a continuous spectrum. Above the photosphere lies a layer of gas at much lower pressure, termed the chromosphere. On its own, the gases in the chromosphere would yield bright lines, but seen against the rainbow background these lines are 'reversed', and appear dark. Their positions and intensities are unaltered, so that they can be identified. In the yellow part of the solar spectrum there are two prominent dark lines; these correspond to the bright lines of sodium – and therefore we can prove that there is sodium in the Sun. By now over 70 elements have been identified in the solar spectrum.

The most abundant element in the whole of the Universe

is the gas hydrogen, the lightest of all substances, and the Sun contains a great deal of it; in fact about 71 per cent of the Sun is hydrogen. Next comes the second lightest gas, helium (27 per cent). All the other elements combined account for only about 2 per cent of the Sun's mass. And armed with this information, we can now work out how the Sun is shining.

It is not 'burning' in the conventional sense. A sun made up entirely of coal, burning as fiercely as the real Sun actually does, would be reduced to ashes in only a few million years, whereas we know that the Sun is around 5,000 million years old. The 'fuel' is hydrogen. Deep in the solar core, where the temperature is of the order of 15 million degrees and the pressures are colossal, the nuclei of hydrogen atoms are combining to form nuclei of helium. It takes four hydrogen nuclei to make up one nucleus of helium; every time this happens a little energy is released, and a little mass (or 'weight', if you like) is lost. It is this energy which keeps the Sun radiating, and the loss in mass amounts to some 4 million tonnes every second. The Sun 'weighs' much less now than it did when you started to read this page. But please do not be alarmed; there is plenty of hydrogen left, and the Sun will not change dramatically for several thousands of millions of years in the future.

The Sun's chromosphere is visible with the naked eye only during a total eclipse (see Picture 3), when the bright surface is hidden by the dark body of the Moon, though spectroscopes can be used to study it at any time. Rising from it are the prominences, which are regions of hot hydrogen gas, reddish in colour – they were once, misleadingly, known as 'Red Flames', and it was only during the mid-19th century that astronomers became sure that they belonged to the Sun rather than to the Moon. Eruptive prominences move and change quickly, and may reach heights of over 60,000 miles

(100,000 km), while quiescent prominences may persist for months.

Above the chromosphere we come to the corona, which may be regarded as the Sun's outer atmosphere. It too is visible with the naked eye only during totality, and it is none too easy to study with conventional spectroscopes, though much has been learned about it since the start of the Space Age in October 1957; artificial satellites are ideal solar observatories, since they move above the Earth's own atmosphere. The corona has no definite boundary, but simply thins out until the density is no greater than that of the usual interplanetary medium. Its density is low – less than one million millionth of that of the Earth's air at sea level – but its temperature rises to around 2 million degrees, which at first sounds rather surprising. However, the scientific definition of temperature differs from what we usually call heat. Temperature is a measure of the average speeds at which the various atoms and molecules move around; the greater the speeds, the higher the temperatures. In the corona the speeds are very great, and so the temperature is high, but there are so few atoms and molecules that the actual amount of heat is negligible. There is an analogy here with a firework sparkler compared with a red-hot poker. Each spark is at a high temperature, but is of such low mass that it is quite safe to hold the sparkler in one's hand – whereas I for one would be reluctant to grasp the end of a glowing poker. Regions in the corona where the temperatures and pressures are below normal are termed coronal holes, and these are associated with what is termed the solar wind, made up of a continuous stream of electrically-charged particles sent out in all directions.

There are many other aspects of solar research. For example there are the violent, short-lived outbreaks known as flares, usually associated with active spot-groups; and, predictably, the Sun is a source of radio emissions which are studied with instruments known, perhaps rather misleadingly, as radio telescopes (most people will have heard of the great 250-foot (76.2-metre) 'dish' radio telescope at Jodrell Bank in Cheshire). But to go into more detail is beyond my scope here; all I have tried to do is to present a general picture. It is now time to turn our attention to eclipses themselves.

Chapter 4

ECLIPSES OF DIFFERENT KINDS

Eclipses of the Sun are of three types: total, annular and partial. All are interesting, but for sheer grandeur total eclipses are unrivalled. Only then can the chromosphere, the prominences and the corona be seen with the naked eye.

Total eclipses occur when the Sun, the Moon and the Earth are exactly lined up, so that the Moon's shadow reaches the surface of the Earth. But as Figure 5 shows, the shadow is only just long enough to do this, and totality can be seen from only a very restricted area of the Earth's surface – which explains why from any particular location, eclipses of the Sun are much less common than those of the Moon. The width of the track of totality can never be more than 169 miles (272 km), and is usually less: to either side of the main cone of the shadow the Sun is only partly hidden. Moreover, totality is brief. From any one site it can never last for longer than 7 minutes 31 seconds, and so far as I know there has never been an observation of an eclipse as protracted as this; the record appears to be held by the 1955 totality as seen from the Philippine Islands, which lasted for 7 minutes 8 seconds. The last English total eclipse, that of 29 June 1927, lasted for a mere 24 seconds, and the width of the track of totality was only 32 miles (52 km). (Note that I say 'English' rather than

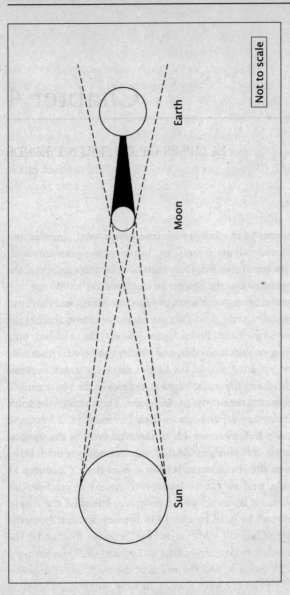

Not to scale

Figure 5: Positions of the Sun, Moon and Earth during a total solar eclipse.

'British'. This is because the track of totality on 30 June 1954 just brushed Unst, the northernmost of the Shetland Islands.)

There is, of course, one way to overcome this problem. To prolong totality as long as possible, the eclipse should take place near the equator where the Earth's rotational velocity reaches a maximum value of a little over 1,000 miles per hour (nearly 1,700 km per hour) from west to east. This cancels out some of the motion of the Moon's shadow which travels at about 2,100 miles per hour (3,400 km per hour) from east to west. Modern supersonic aircraft can fly faster than the resulting minimum speed of just over 1,000 miles per hour with which the Moon's shadow moves over the Earth. During the eclipse of 3 June 1973, a specially-adapted Concorde flew underneath the shadow, keeping pace with it and enabling astronomers on board to enjoy a totality lasting for 1 hour 12 minutes. From a height of 55,000 feet (16,800 m) they had perfect seeing conditions, and were able to watch definite changes in the corona and prominences.* Unfortunately, hiring and adapting a Concorde is a decidedly expensive operation!

Some eclipses are not total from anywhere on Earth, as shown in Picture 4 and Figure 6. Such, for instance, was the eclipse of 12 October 1996; as seen from London just over 60 per cent of the solar disk was hidden. The partial eclipse due on 5 February 2000 will be visible only from the Antarctic, so that it will not be widely appreciated, except possibly by penguins. At maximum phase, 58 per cent of the Sun will be obscured.

---

*Two holes were bored in the Concorde for use by the various scientific instruments to be carried. During the flight, the aircraft passed over Africa, from where other investigators were due to fire a high-altitude rocket capable of making measurements during totality. I feared that if the rocket went off at the wrong moment, there might be three holes in the Concorde; but luckily this did not happen.

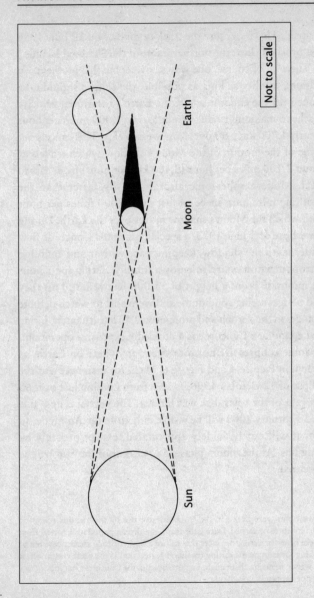

Figure 6: Positions of the Sun, Moon and Earth during a partial solar eclipse.

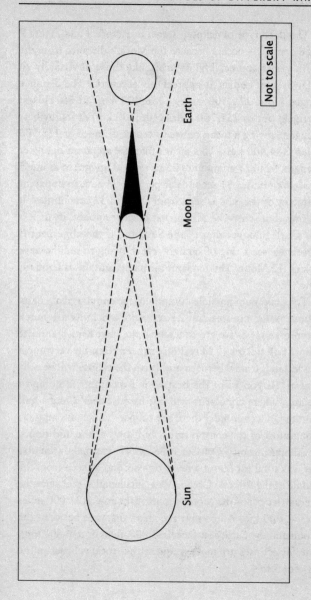

Figure 7: Positions of the Sun, Moon and Earth during an annular solar eclipse.

The third type of eclipse, shown in Picture 5 and Figure 7 – the annular – occurs because the Moon's distance from the Earth varies appreciably; its orbit, like those of virtually all Solar System bodies, is appreciably eccentric. The distance ranges from 221,500 miles (356,400 km) at its closest (perigee) out to 252,700 miles (406,700 km) at its furthest (apogee), giving a mean centre to centre distance of 238,900 miles (384,400 km). This means that the apparent diameter changes, from 29 arcminutes 22 seconds at apogee to as much as 33 arcminutes 31 seconds at perigee. The mean apparent diameter of the Sun as seen from Earth is 32 arcminutes. It follows that when the Moon is at or near apogee, its disk is too small to cover that of the Sun, and if the alignment is perfect we see a ring of sunlight left showing round the dark disk of the Moon. This explains the name; annulus is Latin for 'ring'.

The maximum possible duration of the annular phase of an eclipse is 12 minutes and 24 seconds, but most are much shorter; so far as we are concerned, the next British annular eclipse will fall on 31 May 2003, as seen from the very north of Scotland; from Aberdeen and Perth the eclipse will be only partial. (If you want the best view I recommend going to Iceland, where annularity will last for just over 3 and a half minutes.) Occasionally there are eclipses which are annular along most of the central track, but total at the mid-point. This happened on 3 October 1986, which was mainly annular but was total for about a tenth of a second as seen from the middle of the Atlantic Ocean. Note, incidentally, that since the average length of the Moon's cone of shadow (231,000 miles or 372,000 km) is less that the mean distance between the Moon and the Earth's surface (233,800 miles or 376,300 km), annular eclipses are more frequent that total eclipses in the ratio of 5 to 4.

Eclipse records go back a long way, and the Chinese were particularly interested in spectacular phenomena of this sort, but of course they had no idea of what was happening. They were decidedly dragon-minded, and were of the opinion that during an eclipse a hungry monster was trying to gobble up the Sun. The only remedy was to beat drums, bang gongs, scream and shout, and make as much noise as possible in order to scare the brute away. Not surprisingly, this always worked. One famous story goes back to the reign of the Emperor Chung K'ang, in 2136 BC, and has been widely repeated, though it is quite definitely apocryphal. It is said that the two court astrologers, Hsi and Ho, had failed to predict the eclipse, so that no due warning had been given, and the Emperor was so irate that he had the luckless astrologers executed.

Yet how could eclipses be predicted at all in those far-off times? The answer lies in a curious relationship known as a Saros. It happens that the Sun, Earth and Moon return to almost the same relative positions after a period of 6585.321 solar days, or roughly 18 years 11 days, so that any eclipse tends to be followed by another eclipse in the same Saros series 18 years 11 days later. (In fact, our leap years sometimes turn the 11 days into 10 or 12 days.) The relationship is not exact; for instance the eclipse of 29 June 1927 was total over parts of England, while the 'return' of 9 July 1945 was not; the track crossed Greenland and parts of northern Europe, but from London only 52 percent of the Sun was hidden. A Saros series consists of many individual Saros cycles, and lasts between 1200 and 1500 years. There may be between 69 and 86 eclipses in a Saros series.

It seems that the Babylonians knew about the Saros cycle, more than 2,500 years ago. The Greeks certainly did, and it may well be that a successful prediction was made for 25 May,

585 BC, by Thales, first of the great Greek philosophers. The eclipse took place near sunset in the Mediterranean area, and is said to have brought an abrupt end to a battle between the armies of King Alyattes of the Lydians and King Cyaxares of the Medes. The soldiers were so alarmed by the sudden darkness that they concluded a hasty peace. Some scholars have cast doubt upon this tale, but there is nothing improbable about it, and the later Greeks were well aware that an eclipse is due to the passing of the Moon in front of the Sun. So were the Romans, and a statement made publicly by the Emperor Claudius, in August AD 45, is undoubtedly authentic. Claudius had been literally 'pitchforked' into the role of Emperor following the murder of his predecessor, Caligula, and – rather to everyone's surprise – proved to be an extremely capable ruler; he was also a scholar, and when he realised that an eclipse was due on his birthday he felt compelled to put out an announcement. To quote the Roman writer Dion Cassius, Claudius 'put forth a public notice, not only that the obscuration would take place, and about the time and magnitude of it, but also about the causes that produce such an event'.

Modern computers make it possible to predict eclipses for centuries ahead, if need be. Meanwhile, Table 2 presents a list of the eclipses due between the present time and 2003 – though, of course, not all are visible from anywhere in the British Isles.

The track of the total eclipse of 20 March 2015 will just miss northern Scotland, but covers the Faroe Islands. On 3 September 2081, the track misses England, but crosses the Channel Islands. But for the next totality in the west of England we must wait until 23 September 2090. I fear that I will not see this one – unless of course, I live to the advanced age of a hundred and sixty-seven.

Table 2: Eclipses of the Sun, 1998–2003

Date	Time of mid-eclipse GMT	Type	Max. duration (if total or annular)	Per cent eclipsed (if partial)	Area
22 Aug 1998	02h 7m	Annular	3m 14s		Indian Ocean, Malaysia, Indonesia & Pacific
16 Feb 1999	06h 34m	Annular	40s		Indian Ocean, Australia & Pacific.
11 Aug 1999	11h 03m	Total	2m 23s		Atlantic, west England, Europe, Turkey, Iraq, Iran, Pakistan & India
5 Feb 2000	12h 49m	Partial		58	Antarctica
1 July 2000	19h 32m	Partial		48	Pacific & South America.
31 July 2000	02h 13m	Partial		60	Canada, Alaska, Greenland & Russia
25 Dec 2000	17h 35m	Partial		72	Canada, USA, Mexico & Caribbean
21 June 2001	12h 04m	Total	4m 57s		Atlantic, southern Africa & Indian Ocean.
14 Dec 2001	20h 52m	Annular	3m 53s		Pacific & Central America
10 June 2002	23h 44m	Annular	23s		Indonesia & Pacific
4 Dec 2002	07h 31m	Total	2m 04s		Southern Africa, Indian Ocean & Australia
31 May 2003	04h 08m	Annular	3m 37s		Greenland, Iceland & Scotland.
23 Nov 2003	22h 49m	Total	1m 57s		Antarctica

39

Chapter 5

TOTALITY

We come now to totality – and what we may expect to see on 11 August 1999, clouds permitting. The spectacle should be breathtaking by any standards, and perhaps I may be allowed to begin by quoting from my diary for 30 June 1954, when I saw my first total eclipse. The eclipse was just total from the northernmost part of Unst in the Shetlands, but the main track crossed Scandinavia. The combined party of the Royal Astronomical Society and the British Astronomical Association, of which I was a member, made its headquarters in the little Swedish town of Lysekil, along the coast from Göteborg. Our arrival there coincided with the Midsummer Festival. It also coincided with a burst of torrential rain, but luckily the weather improved at the vital time. My notes run as follows:

On 30 June, most observers collected their equipment and drove to Stromstad, in the exact centre of the track, almost on the Norwegian border. The site selected was a hill overlooking Stromstad itself, and by noon it was littered with equipment of all kinds: telescopes, spectroscopes, cameras, thermometers, and even a large roll of white paper that I had spread out in the hope of recording shadow bands. These are curious narrow, wavy bands of light and dark, which are sometimes seen moving across the ground just before and just after totality. They are due to atmospheric effects, and are none too easy to photograph.

The early stages of the eclipse were well seen. Five minutes before totality, everything became strangely still, and over the hills we could see the approaching area of gloom. Then, suddenly totality was upon us. The corona flashed into view round the dark body of the Moon, a glorious aureole of light which made one realise the inadequacy of a mere photograph. The sky was fairly clear; although a very thin layer of cloud persisted, but only those with the experience of former eclipses could appreciate that we were not seeing the phenomenon in its full splendour.

It was not really dark. Considerable light remained, and of the stars and planets only Venus shone forth. Yet the eclipsed Sun was a superb sight indeed, with brilliant inner corona and conspicuous prominences. The two and a half minutes of totality seemed to race by. Then a magnificent red-gold flash heralded the reappearance of the chromosphere; there was the momentary effect of the 'diamond ring', and then totality was over, with the corona and the prominences lost in the glare and the world waking once more to its everday life. In a few minutes, it was almost as though the eclipse had never been.

Perhaps my best method here will be to list the events of a total eclipse in chronological order, beginning with the first contact of the Moon's disk on the brilliant face of the Sun and ending with fourth contact, the moment when the last portion of the Moon leaves the Sun's disk.

First Contact

A tiny 'notch' appears at the Sun's limb, as shown in Picture 6a. Of course the exact moment can be predicted with great accuracy, but it takes a few seconds for the notch to become noticeable. Naked-eye viewing with suitable dark filters is quite acceptable, but remember to take the greatest care at all times.

Gradually the Moon passes on to the face of the Sun. For a surprisingly long time there is no perceptible diminution in light or fall in temperature, but when the Sun is more than half covered (see Picture 6b) these effects start to become evident. If there are any sunspots (as there probably will be in August 1999) compare them with the darkness of the Moon; the lunar disk will be seen to be much the blacker.

Crescents

By the time that the Sun is nearly half covered, anyone standing near a tree or bush will be able to see tiny crescent-shaped images on the ground around them. Gaps in the foliage act as 'pinhole cameras' and focus the images of the crescent Sun.

Shadow Bands

I have already mentioned shadow bands, which are purely atmospheric phenomena. They are often seen just before totality (and just after), but not always; conditions have to be exactly right. They are surprisingly difficult to photograph. I have made attempts at several eclipses, including that of 1954, but I have never yet had any luck.

Lunar Shadow

As totality approaches, the whole scene changes with amazing rapidity. The temperature falls, the sky darkens, and the shadow of the Moon can be seen rushing across the landscape – or, better, seascape.

The 'Diamond Ring'

Just before the last sliver of the solar photosphere disappears, we see the effect termed the 'Diamond Ring', shown in Picture 7 – a brilliant point which lasts for an all-too-brief period. It is usually better seen at the end of totality, as illustrated in Picture 8.

Baily's Beads

The Moon's limb is not smooth; there are high mountains and deep valleys. Moments before totality, the sunlight comes to us through the lunar valleys on the limb, and the result is a series of bright points of light. They seem to have been first recorded by Edmond Halley (of comet fame) during the eclipse of 1715, but were described in detail during the 1836 eclipse by the English astronomer, Francis Baily, and are named after him. In fact the 1836 eclipse was not total, but annular, so that during a 'short annular', when the Moon's disk is almost large enough to cover the Sun, Baily's beads are quite conspicuous. They are not likely to be seen during the next British annular, that of 31 May 2003, because the Moon will be near apogee, and will cover no more than 94 per cent of the Sun.

Second Contact

The Sun is wholly hidden, and totality has begun. The corona and prominences flash into view; the sky is dark, and almost at once bright stars and planets can be seen. There is an abrupt fall in temperature; birds, understandably confused, start to roost, and some types of flowers to close. There is often a strange, somewhat eerie calm.

The corona is not always of the same shape. Sometimes it displays only short, stumpy streamers (see Picture 9). Near sunspot minimum it sends out 'wings' and streamers, as shown in Picture 10, while near maximum it is more symmetrical – though of course no hard and fast rules can be laid down. Neither can we predict what prominences will be visible, if any, though in this respect the prospects for 1999 seem good.

Mid-totality

Again no two eclipses are alike, but all in all it is fair to say that the corona gives out about as much light as the full moon. This means that direct viewing, even with a telescope, is safe. Pause to look round the sky; any bright planets will shine forth, together with bright stars, though if there is any trace of haze or thin cloud it is likely that only Venus and Jupiter, if favourably placed, will be obvious.

Third contact

Totality ends as suddenly as it had begun. Baily's beads should reappear, and then –

The Diamond Ring

This is one of the most glorious moments of the entire eclipse, and all solar photographers will be on the alert, because it lasts for so short a time. In a few seconds the photosphere starts to reappear; the corona fades from view, and the Diamond Ring is lost. This is certainly the most dangerous moment for the careless observer. The slightest sliver of the main photosphere is as dangerous as the uneclipsed Sun itself

– and so if you have been viewing directly, make sure you take your eye away from the 'danger-zone' in time. Remember, too, that an SLR camera acts in the same way as a telescope or binocular lens.

Partial phase

Gradually the Moon moves off the face of the Sun. The sky quickly brightens: birds unroost (if that is the term!) and flowers open; the Earth seems to 'wake up'. With luck you may see the effects of the receding shadow of the Moon in the form of a curved dark, sometimes purplish patch covering part of the sky, as shown in Pictures 11a and b.

Fourth contact

The Moon finally moves off the Sun, and everything is back to normal; the eclipse is well and truly over. In fact, it usually happens that few observers wait to see the fourth contact; they are too busy packing up their equipment and comparing notes.

Such is the sequence of events for a total eclipse seen under ideal conditions, Sadly, this does not often happen. If there is any cloud around, the outer corona will be lost and no stars or planets will be seen. It may happen that the sky is partly cloudy, in which case all that can be done is to hope for the best. But given clear skies on 11 August 1999, viewers in Cornwall and Devon should see all the phenomena listed here – perhaps even the shadow bands.

Chapter 6

ECLIPSE-WATCHING

In 1968 I went to Siberia to see a total eclipse. Our party made its way to Yurgamysh, and set up our equipment in a decidedly chilly and barren landscape. Suddenly I came across an eminent solar astronomer, Dr Houtgast of Holland, who seemed to be delightfully unconcerned. So far as I could make out, his apparatus consisted solely of an armchair, and I was intrigued. 'What are you going to do?'

He beamed at me. 'I have been to many eclipses. I have observed many eclipses. I have never had time to watch an eclipse. So this time, I do absolutely nothing !' And nor did he. During totality he simply laid back in his chair and enjoyed the spectacle – all one and a half minutes of it.

He was, of course, being eminently sensible. Professional eclipse observers have no time to 'look'; they are far too busy – and this was even more important in past years than it is now, when space research has come so much to the fore. But the same also applies to amateurs, who are so intent on taking photographs and making measurements that they completely fail to take in the grandeur of the scene. This will certainly be the case again on 11 August 1999, and my advice is to set aside a definite period to 'look' and marvel. I appreciate that even if you are sited in the most favourable place – Falmouth, for example – you will have no more than around two minutes of totality, but on no account let your desire to do some photography spoil your appreciation of the superb beauty of the corona.

I have been to several eclipses, and I suppose that I have made most of the mistakes that it is possible to make, so that it may be useful to mention some of the 'traps' into which the unwary can so easily fall. I do not propose to say much here about more technical observations, such as spectroscopy, because this would be beyond the scope of a short booklet, and in any case, serious observers will know more about eclipses than I do, so that all I can attempt here is to give some general advice.

First: make absolutely sure that you know exactly what you mean to do. Well before the eclipse, assemble your equipment, check it, and then carry out a series of rehearsals. You cannot rehearse too often; remember, a single mistake will mean that your chance has gone.

Even if you plan to do no more than 'look' at the eclipse, make sure that you have adequate filters, which are absolutely safe for solar viewing. Staring at the Sun through ordinary sun-glasses, even dark ones, is certainly asking for trouble; these give no protection whatsoever, and neither do exposed photographic film, photographic filters, crossed polarisers, gelatin filters, compact discs, or smoked glass. Please DO NOT be tempted to use any of these.

Welder's glass, rated at number 14 or higher, is suitable for observing the partial phases of the eclipse, but it may be difficult to obtain. Another good material for safe solar filters is aluminised mylar. Mylar is a very tough plastic film, and solar filters are made by coating it with a thin layer of aluminium. The partial phases of the eclipse may be observed safely through a pair of mylar 'spectacles' or 'solar eclipse

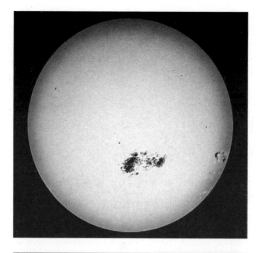

Pictures 1a and b: Full disk image of the Sun (top) showing a large sunspot group, and a composite photograph of the Moon (from images obtained at 1st and 3rd quarter, bottom). Although the Moon is 400 times smaller than the Sun it is 400 times closer to us and so, by a remarkable cosmic coincidence, the two bodies appear almost exactly the same apparent size in the sky.

Picture 2: A demonstration of the correct way to use a small refracting telescope to project the image of the Sun onto a white screen during a partial solar eclipse.

Picture 3: The Sun's chromosphere may only be seen with the naked eye during a total eclipse. Rising from this layer are the reddish prominences – the so-called 'red flames' – which were clear during the rather short 45-second total eclipse in India in 1995.

Picture 4: The partial solar eclipse of 20 July 1982, which occurred shortly before sunset, photographed from Hyde Park in London.

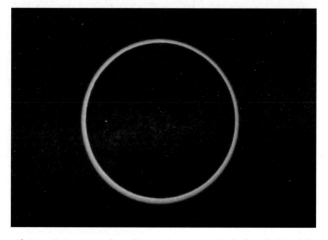

Picture 5: In an annular eclipse a ring or 'annulus' of sunlight is left around the Sun at mid-eclipse because the Moon appears too small in the sky to completely cover the brilliant solar disk.

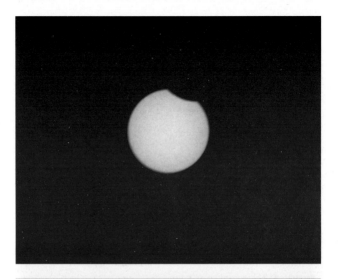

Pictures 6a and b: The partial phases preceding a total solar eclipse: shortly after 'first contact' (top) as the Moon's dark disc encroaches on the Sun, and when the Moon is obscuring nearly half of the Sun (bottom).

Picture 7: A brilliant Diamond Ring and Baily's Beads captured just before the onset of totality.

Picture 8: The unusual broad Diamond Ring seen at the end of the total eclipse from India in 1995.

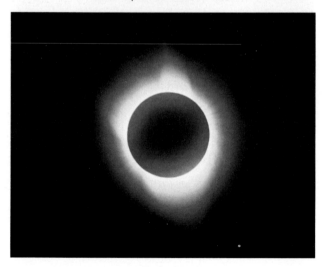

Picture 9: Sometimes the solar corona displays only short, stumpy streamers during totality.

Picture 10: Near sunspot minimum, the solar corona often has prominent equatorial streamers.

Pictures 11a and b: Two views, a few moments apart, showing the Moon's umbral shadow racing away eastwards across the volcano-strewn Chilean Altiplano immediately after totality during the 1994 eclipse.

viewer', and many mylar filters will be available for the 1999 eclipse; but make quite sure that they are genuine – mylar does look rather like kitchen foil!

DO make sure that any filters you use carry the 'CE' mark, and a statement to the effect that they are safe for direct solar viewing. (The 'CE' mark indicates that a filter has been certified under the provisions of the Personal Protective Equipment (EC Directive) Regulations 1992 for the UK and Council Directive 89/686/EEC for the European Union.) Before each use check them very carefully for any damage. DO NOT use filters if they are scuffed, scratched or have holes in them, and DO NOT use any filter if you are not certain that it is approved and safe, or if you have any other doubts about it.

Always hold the filter close to your face and firmly over both your eyes BEFORE looking up at the Sun, and do not remove it until AFTER looking away. DO NOT walk or run when using the solar filter; keep still and in a comfortable position. Also, DO NOT be tempted to look at the Sun, even for a second, without using the filter. Most important of all, DO NOT look at the Sun through any optical instrument, e.g. telescope, binoculars or camera, even if you are wearing special filters.

You can mount layers of sheet mylar over the front object-glass of a telescope or the twin objectives of binoculars, but ONLY do this if you are absolutely certain what you are doing, and make sure that it is so firm that it cannot fall off, be blown off by a gust of wind, or wrinkle without warning.

ONLY during totality, when the Moon completely covers the Sun's brilliant disk, can you put the filters aside and view the totally eclipsed Sun directly without any filter to see the faint and beautiful corona. However, DO be alert to the reappearance of the Sun's brilliant disk at the end of totality. As soon as the first light of the Sun has reappeared you MUST look away immediately and use the special filters once more.

One very simple piece of apparatus which you can use for observation of the partial phases of the eclipse is the 'pinhole camera'. First make a small hole in a piece of stout card, by pushing a needle through it, and then aim the card at the Sun (by means of the shadow); the image can be projected onto a white screen placed a few feet (about a metre) behind the first card. The advantage here is that you are using the method of projection, so that there is no risk at all, but DO NOT look at the Sun through the pinhole; look only at the projected image. It sounds crude, and indeed it is, but it can be surprisingly effective. It is also possible to project the Sun's image by using binoculars. The best method is to keep the cover on one of the objectives and fix a sheet of cardboard round the other, to act as a screen for a second sheet of card or white paper placed behind the eyepiece of that half of the binoculars. Align the binoculars by means of the shadow; make the shadow on the screen as small and sharp as possible, and you can then bring the Sun's image into view. What you MUST NOT do is to try and align the binoculars by looking through them, or even by squinting along the top of the tube.

I will say more about photography later; for the moment it is enough to note that ordinary, non-complicated cameras can be used, though you will need a telephoto lens to obtain an image of reasonable size. Some people, however, prefer to make drawings of the corona, which is not difficult for anyone with artistic ability. We can only hope that in 1999 the scene will be enhanced by at least one brilliant prominence.

Clouds are, of course, the main enemy of the eclipse watcher, but even if things look gloomy it is a mistake to give up too early. I proved this to my own satisfaction from Talikud Island, in the Philippines, at the eclipse of 1988.* Ten minutes before totality, rain was falling. Almost everyone dismantled their equipment. I did not – and with about half a minute to go, there was a break in the clouds; it lasted through totality, and I was at least able to take one reasonable picture.

On the other hand there are, inevitably, occasions when cloud cover totally obscures the eclipsed Sun, and under these circumstances there is nothing to be done about it. Such was the experience of our party in Finland on 22 July 1990. We did our best to find a clear area, but with no success. Even so, it was an interesting experience; the drop in light during totality was quite eerie, the colours of the clouds as the shadow passed by were beautiful, and there was a noticeable fall in temperature.

There are various other things to do – if you have time. Making regular temperature measurements is interesting, for example, and also taking note of the way in which animals and birds behave. Also, you can set up a camera and take a picture of the scene every 10 minutes, say, with the same exposure time; the resulting series can be quite graphic.

Next: what should be avoided at all costs? First, the use of flash photography. This should be self-evident since it would be rather difficult to illuminate the disk of the Moon over a range of around a quarter of a million miles (400,000 km), but I did hear of one enthusiast who decided to flash-photograph the scene during totality, with the result that several pictures were ruined and the culprit became

---

*At the time there were three groups of terrorists in that part of the Philippines. All of them were blowing things up, but they also blew up each other. As we arrived, the three groups issued a combined press statement to the effect that we were nobody's enemy, and they did not propose to blow us up. Frankly, I thought that this was extremely sporting of them.

unpopular, to put it mildly. Secondly, make sure that you keep well away from your nearest neighbour: in the gloom it is only too easy to blunder into someone else's tripod.

The sky during totality is fascinating, and can occasionally produce major surprises. This happened in 1882, when photography was still primitive judged by modern standards. Totality was seen from Egypt; when the pictures were developed, they showed not only the eclipsed Sun, but also a bright comet. The comet had never been seen before, and it was never seen again, so that this is our only record of it. The bright comet of 1948 was also discovered during the eclipse of that year (November 1), though it was subsequently recovered and tracked.

I am not suggesting that there is much chance of another cometary discovery in 1999, but it cannot be ruled out. Years ago, periodical searches were also made for the planet Vulcan, believed to orbit the Sun closer-in than Mercury. However, we now know that Vulcan does not exist, so that wasting further time in looking for it would be rather pointless.

Eclipse-watching is, after all, largely a matter of common sense, but I make no apology for ending these brief notes with a repeat warning. Make absolutely sure that your eyes are fully protected. The main danger comes at the end of totality, because the first segment of the Sun reappears with startling suddenness – and is instantly hazardous. Be prepared for it.

Chapter 7

THE ECLIPSE OF 1927

The last total eclipse visible from any part of England or Wales occurred on 29 June 1927. The track, shown in Figure 8, crossed the coast of Cardigan Bay and then out over the sea. It crossed the coastline of England at Southport, and then proceeded over Preston, Clitheroe, Settle, Richmond, Darlington and Hartlepool; it then crossed the North Sea, and passed over parts of Norway, including the town of Stavanger. Since this was the first British totality since 1724, it caused a great deal of interest, and extensive preparations were made to observe it. (I did not take part, because I was only four years old, and lived in Bognor Regis.)

The Sun was near the peak of its 11-year cycle, and so the corona was expected to be of the maximum type – that is to say, reasonably symmetrical; prominences might also be expected. On the debit side, totality was short, lasting for no more than 24 seconds, and the track was narrow, measuring only 16 miles to either side of the central line. Everything depended upon the weather – and in the event, Nature did not smile. It was cloudy over much of the track, and there were few places from which conditions were good. One of these, fortunately, was Giggleswick in North Yorkshire, where the party from the Royal Greenwich Observatory had set up its equipment. Another party was able to make observations from an aeroplane, provided by the London *Daily Mail*, and these observations were fairly successful, though the photographs obtained were mediocre; apparently the film used was too slow to allow for the inevitable motion of the aeroplane. Moreover, the observers suffered from numbed hands in the intense cold. Heated, pressurised cabins were not available in 1927.

The best results came from Giggleswick. In the *Journal of the British Astronomical Association* for July, 1927 (vol. 37, page 291) P.J. Melotte reported:

With the 45-foot focus coronagraph, a photograph of the corona was obtained on a scale of 5 inches to the Sun's diameter. The exposure given was 19 seconds on an Ilford Special Rapid plate. The inner corona and prominences are exceedingly well shown, and there are many interesting features. Two large prominences are shown near the north pole of the Sun; at the south pole, over a bright prominence, there is a well-defined double arch. In the north-east quadrant are two large prominences. The corona is considerably disturbed in the equatorial regions, both on the east and west limbs. In both cases the disturbance is associated with large prominences, and the coronal matter near the limb is extremely bright, that on the west limb forming a conspicuous horn to the south of the prominences.

The chromosphere is shown completely round the disk of the Moon, and there are numerous smaller prominences in all latitudes. Two filamentous streams of prominence matter are noticeable features in the north-east quadrant. A very bright spot is shown 3' from the limb over the large prominence associated

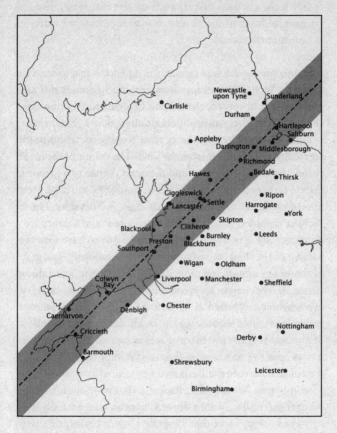

Figure 8: The path of totality across North Wales and northern England during the eclipse of 29 June 1927.

with the coronal disturbance on the east limb. The general form of the corona was that associated with sunspot maximum.

Certainly the corona was spectacular, and according to another observer, W. Porthouse, nno long coronal streamers nor any plumes were observed, the corona being distinctly of a type characteristic of sunspot maximum. Some extensions, comparatively short, of the corona were seen, at no point reaching a full diameter from the limb. The colour of the inner corona was whitish yellow, and the outer corona of a greenish tinge.' Others were less lucky, but made the most of their limited opportunities. From West Witton, in Yorkshire, Huish Webber recorded that 'The Sun rose in mist and totality was obscured. But it was indeed well worth while to have seen the passing of the shadow. Totality came quite suddenly, and gave to the heavy clouds the most awe-inspiring effect of falling closer to the Earth by many thousands of feet. A most overwhelming experience, never to be forgotten. This strange and indescribable shadow was intensely dark, giving the effect of an appalling purply-black. Faces appeared an ashy green; it was like the shadow of death. If it had been of longer duration, I am sure the birds and fowls would certainly have gone to roost. We saw the shadow pass away, but it had no sharp edge.' And C. Walmesley at Clitheroe, where the sky was reasonably clear, wrote that 'birds flew low in circles and sheep stopped feeding. Our dog stopped frisking around and stood still as the total phase approached, gazed at us, then at the sky and crouched down close to us.'

Finally, a report from a non-astronomer, Miss Dorothy Sabin, who described it in a letter to her great grandson, Peter Mittens, who was kind enough to send it to me for publication in a periodical which I then edited. The most vivid part of her account is fascinating. Her observing site was a couple of miles east of Clitheroe, very close to the central line, and the conditions were fairly good:

> Clouds were heavy in the south and west, but soft and fleecy to the east and overhead. The minutes passed slowly, and we spent our time watching the disk of the Moon creeping across the Sun. At 6.10 a.m. there appeared to be the very slightest difference of light; by 6.15 there was a noticeable difference. It was like the twilight of a summer's evening. I turned my back to the Sun, as I had been instructed, and faced south-west.
>
> The light grew dimmer, and we waited in silence. Suddenly, with astonishing rapidity, there came sweeping across the valley and hills, enveloping the whole landscape, a darkness which was soft and clear and transparent, a deep purple grey in colour, and strangely unearthly in appearance.
>
> I was so enthralled with this celestial shadow tearing across the world that I almost forgot everything else. Hurriedly I looked above my head. The sky was a dark blue, flecked with mother-of-pearl clouds, wonderfully luminous. I turned east, and there in the clear sky, between patches of bright cloud, was a black disk entirely surrounded by living flames.
>
> I did not notice Baily's Beads, neither did I see the corona. I had not eyes for anything save those leaping, glowing flames. It seemed hardly more than a second or two that they were visible, for the Moon slipped by, and a tiny slit of Sun appeared; instantly it was daylight once more. The eclipse was over. Down the hillside we scrambled, our thoughts and minds full of the great sight we had seen. It was not till we saw the

morning papers that we learned how disappointed thousands of people had been.

Reading this, one can well understand why the prominences were once known as 'Red Flames'. And since the Sun will again be not too far from the maximum of its cycle in 1999, we may well feel optimistic that we will see the prominences as well as Dorothy Sabin did more than 70 years ago.

Chapter 8

THE 1999 ECLIPSE

If you are planning to go to Cornwall or Devon for the 1999 eclipse, I must sound an immediate note of caution: so far as I know, virtually every hotel, guest house and bed and breakfast in the zone of totality is already booked up. I may be wrong, of course, and there are always last-minute cancellations, but the West Country shows signs of being overcrowded around the time of the eclipse.

Drive down, then, and select a suitable site? There will be problems here too. Even in an ordinary year the roads are jam-packed, and in the days just before the eclipse (which occurs mid-week) the situation is bound to be frustrating. Public transport ought to be the answer, but I fear that trains and coaches may be hopelessly overcrowded, even though the railway companies and tour operators are laying on many extra services, and special trains and coaches are being chartered to ferry people down to the south-west of England for the eclipse. It may be that some roads will be officially closed during 'eclipse week', and the only advice I can give is to make your plans carefully. If you have to drive, start out several days early if you can.

As you can see from the map shown in Figure 9, the track

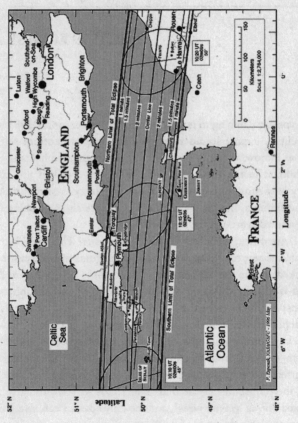

Figure 9: The path of totality through England and France on 11 August 1999.

of totality crosses the Isles of Scilly and then hits Cornwall in the Land's End area. It next traverses the Cornish peninsula, and thence into Devon. Major towns along the track include Hugh Town, Penzance, Helston, Camborne, Redruth, Falmouth, Truro, Newquay, St Austell, Bodmin, Saltash, Plymouth, Kingsbridge, Newton Abbot and Torquay (Torbay), but of course not all of these are close to the centre line; Penzance, Helston and Falmouth are very near to it, but if you stay in Newton Abbot you will have a totality lasting for only half a minute, and from Exeter or Weymouth you will miss it altogether. From towns such as Widecombe and Teignmouth, which are just outside the northern limit of the path of totality, the Sun will be only 99.9 per cent eclipsed, but observers there should witness a magnificent display of Baily's Beads. The track then passes over the English Channel, crosses Alderney in the Channel Islands and moves on into mainland Europe. The northern tip of Guernsey just misses the track, but again observers there should at least see a fine display of Baily's Beads.

Obviously, the closer you are to the central line, the longer the duration of totality, but in most of the favoured sites the duration is around the two-minute mark – 2 minutes 2 seconds in Penzance, Helston and Falmouth, for example, though the mountainous nature of the Moon's limb makes precise predictions difficult, and there may be errors of a few seconds. Some books will give timings for the eclipse which may differ from those listed here by several seconds; in some cases these have used a slightly larger value for the mean diameter of the Moon than that adopted here. However, use of the slightly smaller value for the mean lunar diameter generally gives predictions for the duration of totality which are closer to those actually experienced during total eclipses.

Of course, we are entirely at the mercy of the weather – and we all know about British weather. The eclipse takes place in the morning, with the Sun more than 45 degrees above the horizon, and this is a help. Over the past few years, the hours of sunshine in August have been, on average, 220 in the Channel Islands, 205 in the Isles of Scilly, and about 180 in Devon and Cornwall, but we also have to reckon with sea mist and morning fog, which can be slow to clear. Quite honestly, it is purely a matter of chance. A predominantly cloudy sky may have a fortunate break (as happened at Giggleswick in 1927), whereas a mainly clear sky may produce a patch of cloud in just the wrong place at just the wrong moment. What you will not be able to do in either Cornwall or Devon, I fear, is get into your car and drive quickly to a more promising site. The roads will be far too crowded for that, and you will have no alternative but to stay where you are.

Aircraft flights will no doubt be arranged, but will have to be booked well in advance, and the amount of equipment which can be carried is very limited. The elevation of the Sun during totality (over 45 degrees) may also present problems in some aircraft. However, it would be amazingly unlucky to be forced to remain below cloud level, and if you are prepared for a restricted but virtually certain view this is perhaps the answer.

Table 3 gives the timings for various sites (where the eclipse is total) in Cornwall and Devon, plus the Isles of Scilly and Alderney. Remember that totality begins at Second Contact, and ends at Third Contact; remember also that I have used British Summer Time, which is one hour ahead of Greenwich Mean Time.

It is not possible to forecast the shape of the corona with complete accuracy, but the Sun will be well on the way to the next maximum of its cycle of activity, so that we may expect the corona to be rather more symmetrical than it was during the total eclipses of the earlier 1990s. There is also a better chance of bright prominences, and for these it should be possible to make predictions a day or two before the eclipse, because sunspot and flare activity can be followed.

We also know which planets and stars should be visible, and the general view during totality is given in Figure 10 – drawn for Falmouth in Cornwall, but almost the same for the other regions of the West Country. Venus will be 15 degrees east of the Sun, and at its magnitude of -3.5 should be glaringly obvious; in fact if the sky is clear, Venus will be detectable with the naked eye well before totality and will remain visible for some time after totality has ended. Mercury, 18 degrees west of the Sun, will be of magnitude +0.7, and should be easy enough to locate. Jupiter (magnitude -2.1) and Saturn (magnitude +0.1) will be rather low in the west, and in view of the short duration of totality I would not recommend you to waste any time in looking for them. The Sun itself will be in the barren Zodiacal constellation of Cancer, the crab, but there will be various first magnitude stars on view, notably Sirius in Canis Major, the great dog (magnitude -1.5), Procyon in Canis Minor, the little dog (magnitude +0.4), the two leaders of Orion, Betelgeux (about magnitude +0.5; it is decidedly variable) and Rigel (magnitude +0.1), and Aldebaran in Taurus, the bull (magnitude +0.9). No comets are forecast, but, as I have commented earlier, one never knows.

Various national and local astronomical societies have already chosen and reserved their sites. For instance, the Royal Astronomical Society is holding the 1999 National Astronomy Meeting in Guernsey, and observers will go to Alderney on the morning of the eclipse. The party organised by the British Astronomical Association will be based at Truro School in Cornwall. You may well think it wise to join some definite party; this will make life easier for you, but you will have to apply early.

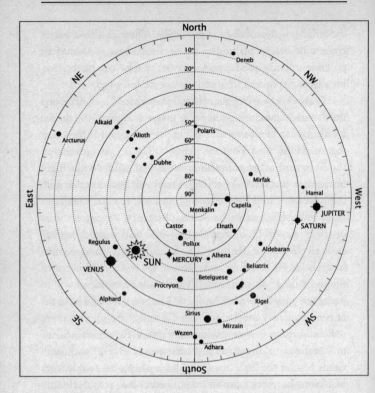

Figure 10: The sky during totality as seen from Falmouth in Cornwall on 11 August 1999.

Naturally, there will be many people who would like to go to the zone of totality, but for various reasons are unable to do so. They will miss the magnificence of the spectacle of totality, but a large partial eclipse is still well worth watching, and if the obscuration is over 99 per cent there is a chance of catching Baily's Beads at least – perhaps, with real luck, a prominence. (I admit that I have never seen a report of a prominence observed with the naked eye other than during totality, but under exceptional conditions it seems to be possible.) Obscuration is over 98 per cent across the whole of Devon and Cornwall, and over 99 per cent in towns such as Okehampton, Exeter, Weymouth and Bournemouth. The timings and obscurations for various major towns and cities in the British Isles are given in Table 4, and Figure 11 shows schematically the partial phases (at maximum eclipse) and the path of totality. London, for example, will witness an obscuration of around 97 per cent, Birmingham 94 per cent and Edinburgh 82 per cent.

Finally, many people will decide that the British weather is too unreliable, so that a holiday abroad may well be combined with eclipse-watching. Northern France is easily accessible, and the eclipse will be total from the Channel ports of Cherbourg, Le Havre, and Dieppe. Inland the zone of totality extends across Rouen, Amiens, Reims, Verdun, Metz and Strasbourg in France. The duration of totality on the centre line increases slightly as the Moon's shadow travels from west to east; from 2m 09s at Cany-Barville (in the Seine-Maritime) to 2m 11s at Noyon (in the Oise) and 2m 15s at Rohrbach-les-Bitche (in the Moselle). Paris, unfortunately, is just south of the zone of totality and enjoys an obscuration of only 99.4 per cent. However, there is plenty of choice elsewhere because the path of totality also crosses the southern tip of Belgium and Luxembourg (including the capital, Luxembourg City), before traversing southern Germany (including the cities of Karlsruhe, Stuttgart, Augsburg and Munich), Austria, and Hungary. It then passes over the extreme north-eastern tip of Yugoslavia, Romania (including the capital, Bucharest), the north-eastern part of Bulgaria, and out over the Black Sea. The greatest duration of totality on the centre line – 2m 23s – takes place near Rimnicu-Vilcea in Romania. (The timings and circumstances for various cities in mainland Europe are listed in Tables 5 and 6).

The Moon's shadow then sweeps across central Turkey, the north-eastern tip of Syria, northern Iraq and central Iran. The path of totality across mainland Europe and the Middle East is shown in the series of maps comprising Figures 12 to 18 inclusive. The eclipse ends at sunset in the Bay of Bengal after passing over southern Pakistan and central India, but the chances of witnessing the eclipse from this far east are slim as the monsoon season will be only just past its peak over Pakistan and India. However, in central Turkey, Iraq and Iran the chances of success are very good, since weather prospects are excellent with a high probability of clear skies.

But personally I prefer to stay in the West Country. Not until 23 September 2090, will people living in Cornwall or Devon have another chance to see the brilliant face of the Sun blotted out by the dark disk of the Moon.

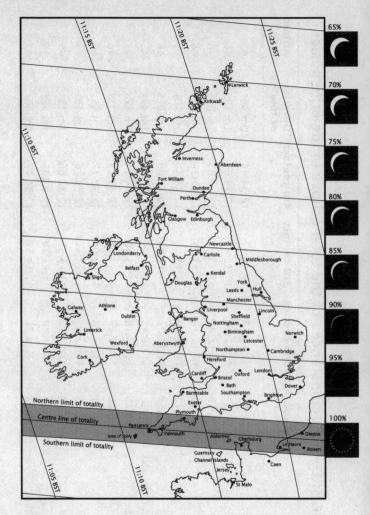

Figure 11: Circumstances of the 11 August 1999 eclipse for the British Isles showing the partial phases (at maximum eclipse) and the path of totality.

Table 3: Local circumstances of the total eclipse in the British Isles

Site	1st contact	2nd contact	3rd contact	4th contact	Duration of totality	Altitude (deg.)
Ashburton	09:58:51	11:13:59	11:14:47	12:34:34	0m 48s	47
Bodmin	09:57:51	11:12:22	11:13:41	12:33:00	1m 19s	46
Camborne	09:56:58	11:11:02	11:13:03	12:32:03	2m 01s	46
Falmouth	09:57:08	11:11:19	11:13:21	12:32:28	2m 02s	46
Fowey	09:57:47	11:12:09	11:13:59	12:33:10	1m 50s	46
Helston	09:56:54	11:11:02	11:13:03	12:32:09	2m 01s	46
Hugh Town (Scilly Isles)	09:55:45	11:09:43	11:11:24	12:30:30	1m 41s	45
Kingsbridge	09:58:35	11:13:18	11:15:10	12:34:34	1m 52s	47
Liskeard	09:58:05	11:12:42	11:14:03	12:33:25	1m 21s	46
Lizard	09:56:51	11:11:08	11:13:01	12:32:17	1m 53s	46
Looe	09:57:58	11:12:25	11:14:11	12:33:26	1m 46s	46
Lostwithiel	09:57:50	11:12:17	11:13:52	12:33:06	1m 35s	46
Newquay	09:57:25	11:11:40	11:13:18	12:32:25	1m 38s	46
Newton Abbot	09:59:00	11:14:21	11:14:51	12:34:47	0m 30s	47

Table 3 continued

Padstow	09:57:43	11:12:19	11:13:15	12:32:40	0m 56s	46
Penzance	09:56:39	11:10:39	11:12:41	12:31:41	2m 02s	46
Plymouth	09:58:17	11:12:54	11:14:33	12:33:54	1m 39s	46
Redruth	09:57:04	11:11:09	11:13:10	12:32:11	2m 01s	46
St. Anne (Alderney)	09:59:39	11:15:21	11:17:02	12:37:15	1m 41s	48
St. Austell	09:57:36	11:11:54	11:13:44	12:32:53	1m 50s	46
St. Ives	09:56:49	11:10:49	11:12:50	12:31:48	2m 01s	46
St. Just	09:56:32	11:10:29	11:12:30	12:31:27	2m 01s	46
St. Mawes	09:57:13	11:11:25	11:13:27	12:32:34	2m 02s	46
Salcombe	09:58:31	11:13:12	11:15:10	12:34:34	1m 58s	47
Saltash	09:58:16	11:12:54	11:14:29	12:33:51	1m 35s	46
Tavistock	09:58:30	11:13:35	11:14:11	12:33:57	0m 36s	46
Torquay (Torbay)	09:59:02	11:14:08	11:15:15	12:34:58	1m 07s	47
Totnes	09:58:49	11:13:43	11:15:09	12:34:41	1m 26s	47
Truro	09:57:18	11:11:28	11:13:25	12:32:29	1m 57s	46
Wadebridge	09:57:48	11:12:34	11:13:25	12:32:49	1m 01s	46

All times are BST (=GMT +1h). Altitude (in degrees) is for mid-eclipse.

Table 4: Local circumstances of the partial eclipse in the British Isles

Site	1st contact	Maximum eclipse	Obscuration (per cent)	Altitude (deg.)	4th Contact
Aberdeen	10:08:28	11:20:05	77.6	43	12:34:42
Belfast	10:01:37	11:14:04	86.8	43	12:30:32
Birmingham	10:02:52	11:17:59	93.5	46	12:37:00
Blackburn	10:03:40	11:17:46	89.2	45	12:35:36
Bournemouth	10:00:56	11:17:04	99.5	48	12:37:29
Brighton	10:02:57	11:19:39	98.8	49	12:40:17
Bristol	10:00:59	11:16:28	97.2	47	12:36:11
Cardiff	10:00:23	11:15:37	97.2	46	12:35:12
Cork	09:56:03	11:09:07	96.3	43	12:27:07
Derby	10:03:41	11:18:39	91.9	46	12:37:22
Dublin	09:59:43	11:12:49	91.2	43	12:30:17
Edinburgh	10:05:47	11:18:04	81.8	43	12:33:45
Exeter	09:59:16	11:14:48	99.7	47	12:34:53
Glasgow	10:04:48	11:16:50	82.2	43	12:32:25
Gloucester	10:01:48	11:17:09	95.7	47	12:36:36
Ipswich	10:05:35	11:21:57	94.2	48	12:41:45
Kingston-upon-Hull	10:05:48	11:20:32	88.8	46	12:38:41
Leeds	10:04:39	11:18:57	88.8	46	12:36:51
Leicester	10:03:47	11:19:03	92.8	47	12:38:05

Table 4 continued

Liverpool	10:02:51	11:17:02	90.5	45	12:35:05
London (Central)	10:03:34	11:19:51	96.6	48	12:39:57
Luton	10:03:41	11:19:39	95.3	48	12:39:24
Manchester	10:03:36	11:17:56	90.1	46	12:36:01
Middlesbrough	10:05:53	11:19:45	86.1	45	12:37:01
Newcastle-upon-Tyne	10:06:03	11:19:31	84.8	45	12:36:21
Northampton	10:03:32	11:19:08	94.2	47	12:38:31
Norwich	10:06:18	11:22:19	92.2	48	12:41:39
Nottingham	10:04:04	11:19:06	91.7	47	12:37:49
Oxford	10:02:41	11:18:27	95.9	47	12:38:10
Portsmouth	10:01:53	11:18:16	99.1	48	12:38:46
Reading	10:02:39	11:18:41	96.9	48	12:38:41
St Peter Port, Guernsey	09:59:03	11:15:35	99.9	48	12:36:45
Sheffield	10:04:12	11:18:51	90.3	46	12:37:09
Southampton	10:01:38	11:17:51	98.8	48	12:38:12
Southend-on-Sea	10:04:34	11:21:08	96.1	49	12:41:19
Stoke-on-Trent	10:03:06	11:17:47	91.8	46	12:36:20
Swansea	09:59:49	11:14:43	96.8	46	12:34:01
Swindon	10:01:55	11:17:37	96.7	47	12:37:24
York	10:05:18	11:19:40	88.2	46	12:37:30

All times are BST (=GMT + 1h). Altitude (in degrees) is for maximum eclipse.
Obscuration (per cent) is the fraction of the Sun obscured at maximum eclipse.

Table 5: Local circumstances of the total eclipse in Europe

Site	1st contact	2nd contact	3rd contact	4th contact	Duration of totality	Altitude (deg.)
Amiens	11:04:55	12:22:05	12:23:56	13:44:40	1m 51s	51
Augsburg	11:15:26	12:35:53	12:38:10	14:00:04	2m 17s	56
Bucharest	11:41:25	13:05:48	13:08:10	14:28:44	2m 22s	59
Cherbourg	11:00:11	12:16:10	12:17:45	13:38:11	1m 35s	49
Dieppe	11:03:30	12:20:09	12:22:10	13:42:39	2m 01s	50
Graz	11:22:09	12:44:57	12:46:09	14:08:56	1m 12s	58
Karlsruhe	11:12:12	12:31:39	12:33:47	13:55:21	2m 08s	54
Le Havre	11:02:03	12:18:49	12:20:20	13:41:14	1m 31s	50
Linz	11:20:36	12:42:41	12:43:11	14:05:39	0m 30s	57
Luxembourg	11:09:30	12:28:21	12:29:41	13:51:13	1m 20s	53
Metz	11:09:13	12:27:56	12:30:09	13:51:35	2m 13s	53
Munich	11:16:21	12:37:12	12:39:20	14:01:26	2m 08s	56
Rimnicu-Vilcea	11:37:55	13:01:59	13:04:21	14:25:15	2m 22s	59
Reims	11:06:32	12:24:36	12:26:35	13:47:56	1m 59s	52
Rouen	11:03:06	12:20:11	12:21:51	13:42:51	1m 40s	50
Saarbrucken	11:10:23	12:29:18	12:31:27	13:52:52	2m 09s	53
Silistra	11:43:47	13:08:14	13:10:35	14:30:49	2m 21s	59
Strasbourg	11:11:03	12:30:59	12:32:23	13:54:40	1m 24s	54
Stuttgart	11:13:09	12:32:55	12:35:12	13:56:54	2m 17s	55
Szeged	11:30:04	12:53:22	12:55:43	14:17:22	2m 21s	59
Timisoara	11:32:01	12:55:52	12:57:54	14:19:42	2m 02s	59

All times are EST (=GMT + 2h). Altitude (in degrees) is for mid-eclipse.

Table 6: Local circumstances of the partial eclipse in Europe

Site	1st contact	Maximum eclipse	Obscuration (per cent)	Altitude (deg.)	4th Contact
Amsterdam	11:10:09	12:27:22	91.9	50	13:47:12
Athens	11:41:26	13:10:14	78.1	66	14:34:30
Belgrade	11:30:54	12:56:24	97.7	60	14:19:54
Berlin	11:21:13	12:39:54	87.2	52	13:59:16
Berne	11:09:47	12:31:17	95.1	56	13:55:21
Brussels	11:08:08	12:26:17	97.4	51	13:47:25
Budapest	11:28:13	12:51:42	99.3	58	14:14:01
Copenhagen	11:22:33	12:38:05	77.3	49	13:54:23
Helsinki	11:41:34	12:51:26	57.0	45	14:00:18
Kiev	11:47:35	13:07:10	79.4	53	14:23:20
Lisbon	10:46:02	11:59:19	59.5	47	13:20:17
Madrid	10:52:43	12:09:55	66.3	52	13:33:41
Minsk	11:42:49	12:59:28	72.2	50	14:13:55
Moscow	11:58:09	13:09:52	58.6	46	14:18:31
Oslo	11:24:38	12:35:29	65.1	45	13:47:14
Paris	11:04:09	12:22:49	99.4	51	13:45:14
Prague	11:21:27	12:42:24	94.6	55	14:03:43
Rome	11:17:16	12:42:39	80.2	63	14:08:52
Sofia	11:36:58	13:03:50	93.6	62	14:27:22
Stockholm	11:32:25	12:43:59	63.3	46	13:55:24
Vienna	11:23:47	12:46:28	99.2	57	14:08:55
Warsaw	11:32:16	12:51:28	82.6	53	14:09:31

Notes: All times are EST (=GMT + 2h). Altitude (in degrees) is for maximum eclipse.
Obscuration (per cent) is the fraction of the Sun obscured at maximum eclipse.

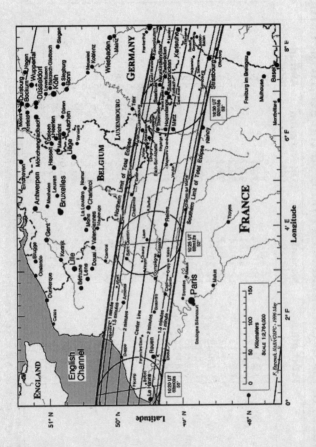

Figure 12: The path of totality through France, Belgium, Luxembourg and Germany on 11 August 1999.

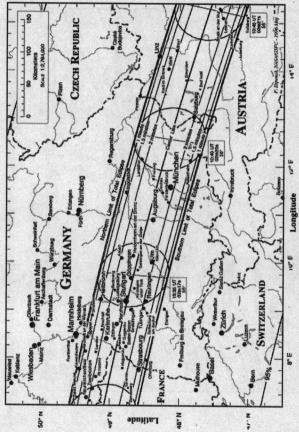

Figure 13: The path of totality through Germany and Austria on 11 August 1999.

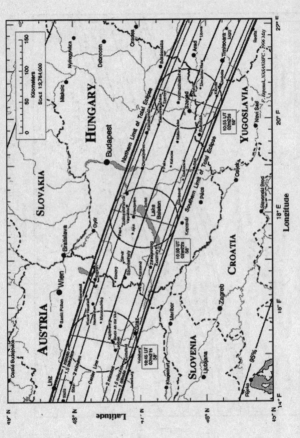

Figure 14: The path of totality through Austria, Hungary and Romania on 11 August 1999.

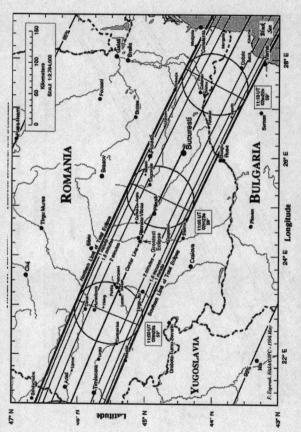

Figure 15: The path of totality through Romania and Bulgaria on 11 August 1999.

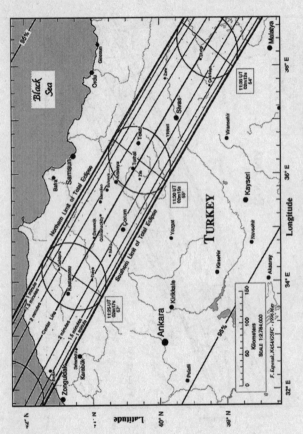

Figure 16: The path of totality through Turkey on 11 August 1999.

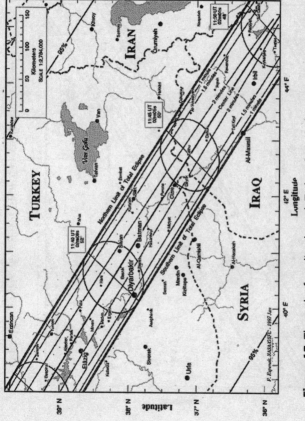

Figure 17: The path of totality through Turkey, Syria and Iraq on 11 August 1999.

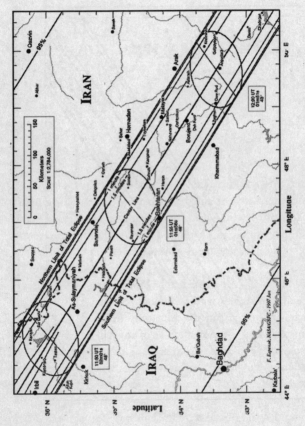

Figure 18: The path of totality through Iraq and Iran on 11 August 1999.

Chapter 9

PHOTOGRAPHING THE ECLIPSE

Watching an eclipse is an amazing experience, but most people will be keen to have a photographic record, and this will certainly be the case on 11 August 1999. Of course, very complicated apparatus can be used. Here, I propose to say virtually nothing about telescopes, video camcorders, CCDs, and spectroscopes and spectrographs, because anyone who uses equipment of that sort will know what they are about. Therefore I will confine myself to trying to give some guidance to the beginner with an ordinary camera.

In fact almost any reasonably good camera will do, but a normal camera lens with a 50 mm focal length will yield an image of the Sun on the film only half a millimetre in diameter, which is too small to be of any real use. This means using a telephoto lens, which makes all the difference; a 500 mm lens will give an image nearly 5 mm across, and if the photograph is sharp enough it can be enlarged. But before going any further, and at the risk of being regarded as paranoid, I feel bound to repeat my warning. During actual totality, it is safe to use any lens and to look direct at the Sun. With the slightest sliver of the photosphere in view, it is not safe, and the total phase both begins and ends with startling suddenness. To photograph the partial phases, you must use your filter (usually mylar), fixed over the front of the camera lens. For totality this must be taken off – and replaced before the brilliant disk of the Sun reappears.

Incidentally, it is a mistake to take too many images of the pre-totality partial phase; you may find that you have used up more of your film than you expect. Far better to wait until after totality for your 'partial' pictures. My usual procedure is to wind off the film showing totality, and then re-load for the final partial phases; by now you have plenty of time to spare – the mad rush is over.

By the way, another trap is to imagine that you have loaded a 36-exposure film when in fact you have only 24. Trying to change a film during totality is emphatically not to be recommended. Also, make sure that everything is in its proper place. I well remember the luckless photographer who took 40 images of the corona under ideal conditions – with his lens-hood in position all the time. He was much displeased.

A cable release is really essential; otherwise you are bound to ruin your pictures because of camera shake. And this brings me on to the necessity of using a sturdy tripod. Hand-holding is quite unsatisfactory; a tripod is easy to transport, and it must be firm – there is no point in using a good camera if you mount it on the equivalent of a blancmange. More photographs of eclipses are spoiled by camera-shake than by any other fault.

Again I stress the importance of rehearsal (it is wise to take photographs of the uneclipsed Sun in the days before totality). Always make sure that your mylar is faultless, with no scratches or pinholes in it, and that it is firmly fixed – but can still be removed quickly and easily with the onset of totality; if it sticks, there is always the chance of knocking

Table 7: Exposure times for solar eclipse photography

Subject	Exp. (s) with Focal ratio f/4	Exp. (s) with Focal ratio f/8
With 50 ISO Film:		
Baily's Beads	1/2000	1/500
Diamond Ring	1/500	1/125
Prominences	1/250	1/60
Inner Corona	1/30	1/8
Outer Corona	1/4	1
Partial Phase	1/2000	1/500
With 100 ISO Film:		
Baily's Beads	1/4000	1/1000
Diamond Ring	1/1000	1/250
Prominences	1/500	1/125
Inner Corona	1/60	1/15
Outer Corona	1/8	1/2
Partial Phase	1/4000	1/1000
With 400 ISO Film:		
Baily's Beads	–	1/4000
Diamond Ring	1/4000	1/1000
Prominences	1/2000	1/500
Inner Corona	1/250	1/60
Outer Corona	1/30	1/8
Partial Phase	–	1/4000

over the whole tripod. This, too, has happened in the past.

Totality in 1999 will be short, so that it is essential to work out in advance just what you hope to do photographically. Different phenomena require different exposures – obviously to record the outer corona you will need a longer exposure than for the inner corona. And at the end of totality, you should be ready to give a much briefer exposure for the re-emerging Diamond Ring. Believe me, those two minutes on 11 August, will seem more like 20 seconds.

There is abundant light, so that you do not need a fast film; an ISO of from 50 to 100 is suitable, though there is no harm in going up to ISO 400 (or even higher if you are carrying out special types of work). The film speeds listed here will be useful as a general guide, but everyone will have their own ideas, and it is always sensible to 'bracket' either side of your mean exposure. Also, once again so much depends on the state of the sky. If you want more detailed recommendations, consult one of the more technical books listed under 'Further Reading' at the end of this booklet; the exposure times given in Table 7 here are those recommended by Michael Maunder in the book, *The Sun in Eclipse*. Times are given in seconds.

Photographing the landscape during totality is interesting; with 50 ISO film at f/8 an exposure of a couple of seconds ought to be about right, and with 100 ISO film at f/8 a single second will do. But again, on no account use flash.

Until almost the very last moment we will not know just what the situation will be on 11 August 1999. We will know the state of the solar cycle, and we may have a good idea of what prominences will be visible, if any; but we will not know about the shape or brightness of the corona, and we will not know whether the sky conditions will allow us to trace the corona out to its limits, or to see the stars. We can only hope. And if we are unlucky, and the sky does prove to be overcast – well, we can always look forward to a return visit to Cornwall on 23 September 2090!

Chapter 10

ECLIPSES OF THE FUTURE

Eclipse-chasing becomes addictive. If you go to the south-west of England on 11 August 1999, I guarantee that you will be fired with enthusiasm, whether you see totality or not. So short of waiting for a good many decades, where can you go to see a repeat performance? The next five total eclipses are given in Table 8.

So far as the British Isles are concerned, the situation is far less promising. It will be much better in the 22nd century, when our islands will see six totalities in just 56 years, but I am afraid that for the readers of this booklet these eclipses are of no more than academic interest. However, it may be worth listing them, just in case this booklet falls in the hands of your great-great-grandchildren ...

20 March 2015	Path of totality misses Britain, but crosses the Faroe Islands where totality lasts for 2m 45s.
3 September 2081	Like 2015, totality misses mainland Britain, but the Channel Islands lie just inside the northern limit of the path of totality.

23 September 2090   Path of totality crosses the southern tip of Ireland, and southern England (including Cornwall and Devon), but centre line misses the mainland so maximum duration is 2m 10s. Eclipse occurs just before sunset, so Sun will be low in western sky (elevation less than 10 degrees).

We then come to the 22nd century:

3 June 2133	Hebrides, northern Scotland and Shetland Islands.
7 October 2135	Southern Scotland and northern England.
25 May 2142	Channel Islands
14 June 2151	Northern Ireland, western Scotland, north-west England, the Midlands, East Anglia, north and east London and parts of Kent
4 June 2160	Southern tip of Ireland and Land's End (just)
8 November 2189	Southern tip of Ireland, Cornwall and Channel Islands

I hope that this brief guide has been of some help to you. All we can do now is to wait for the great day – and keep your fingers crossed that for a few minutes on the morning of Wednesday, 11 August, 1999, the Sun will shine brightly over Cornwall and Devon before being temporarily blotted out by the dark advancing disk of the Moon.

Table 8: The next five total eclipses

Date	Location	Maximum Duration
21 June 2001	Atlantic Ocean, Angola, Zambia, Zimbabwe, Mozambique, Indian Ocean	4m 57s
4 December 2002	Angola, Zambia, Namibia, Botswana-Zimbabwe, South Africa, Mozambique, Indian Ocean, South Australia	2m 04s
23 November 2003	Antarctica, Indian Ocean	1m 57s
8 April 2005	Pacific Ocean, Costa Rica, Panama, Colombia, Venezuela	42s
29 March 2006	Atlantic Ocean, Ghana, Togo, Benin, Nigeria, Niger, Chad, Libya, Mediterranean Sea, Turkey, Georgia, Kazakhstan	4m 07s

Further Reading

Many books about solar eclipses have been published. Among those which relate specifically to the 1999 eclipse are:

BELL, Steve. *The RGO Guide to the 1999 Total Eclipse of the Sun.* HM Nautical Almanac Office, 1997. (£5.99)

HARRINGTON, Philip S. *Eclipse! The What, Where, When, Why & How Guide to Watching Solar & Lunar Eclipses.* John Wiley & Sons, 1997.

MAUNDER, Michael and MOORE, Patrick. *The Sun in Eclipse.* Springer-Verlag, Godalming , 1997. (£18)

WILLIAMS, Sheridan. *UK Solar Eclipses from Year 1.* Clock Tower Press, Leighton Buzzard, 1996. (£7.10)

Index